CU00923753

CLASSIC

THUNDERBIRDS™

The Little Book of

THUNDERBIRD 3

THIS IS A CARLTON BOOK

Published by Carlton Books Limited 2003
20 Mortimer Street
London W1T 3JW

Text and design copyright © 2003 Carlton Publishing Group

™ and © 1964, 1999 and 2003 ITC Entertainment Group Ltd.
THUNDERBIRDS is a Gerry Anderson Production.
Licensed by Carlton International Media Limited.

www.thunderbirdsonline.com

A CIP catalogue record for this book is available from the
British Library.

ISBN 1 84442 897 4

The Little Book of

THUNDERBIRD 3

INTERNATIONAL RESCUE'S SPACE RESCUE ROCKET

CARLTON
BOOKS

CONTENTS

THUNDERBIRD 3

FACT FILE

Thunderbird 3 is International Rescue's massive orange space rocket. It stands an incredible 287 feet high.

Ergonomically simplified flight console: computerized flight system maintains TB3's course and life-support systems, allowing Alan to concentrate on piloting

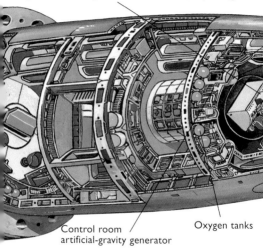

Control room artificial-gravity generator

Oxygen tanks

THUNDERBIRD 3

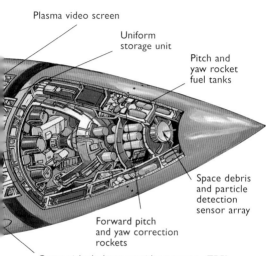

Plasma video screen

Uniform storage unit

Pitch and yaw rocket fuel tanks

Space debris and particle detection sensor array

Forward pitch and yaw correction rockets

Outer airlock door: provides access to TB5's docking-bay gantry. The airlock is gravity-variable to allow pilot's reorientation with TB5's gantry, which is at 90 degrees to TB3's control room

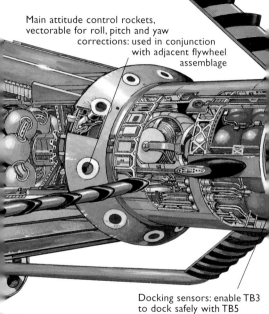

Main attitude control rockets, vectorable for roll, pitch and yaw corrections: used in conjunction with adjacent flywheel assemblage

Docking sensors: enable TB3 to dock safely with TB5

THUNDERBIRD 3

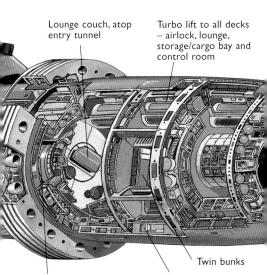

Lounge couch, atop entry tunnel

Turbo lift to all decks – airlock, lounge, storage/cargo bay and control room

Twin bunks

Lounge video monitor, connected to ship's systems, sensors and on-board entertainment systems

Toilet and shower: both have zero-gravity operating options if required

Chemical rocket explosion chamber: chemical rockets are used for take-off and provide extra boost during space flights

Gate seal: blocks off particle accelerator from explosion chamber when rockets are firing

Control and fuel lines connecting propellant tanks to rocket motors

Rear pitch and yaw rockets

Helium-pressurized monatomic propellant tanks for main motors

Entry tunnel air lock door: once the couch from the Tracy Villa lounge has been transported along the service tunnel to TB3's launch bay, it is raised on a hydraulic ram through the airlock doors into the entry tunnel. After the couch has been locked into position on TB3's lounge deck, the ram retracts and the airlock is closed

THUNDERBIRD 3

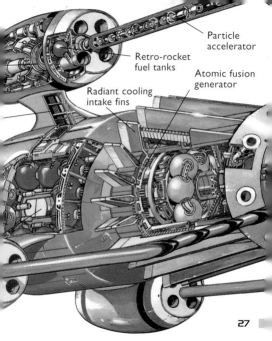

Particle
accelerator

Retro-rocket
fuel tanks

Atomic fusion
generator

Radiant cooling
intake fins

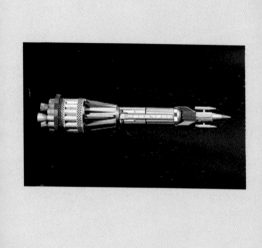

SPACE RESCUES

THE SUN PROBE AFFAIR

The Sun Probe mission would have been a disaster but for International Rescue. Using an ion drive and a chemical rocket system, the Sun Probe's launch thrust of 20 million pounds gave it the acceleration to reach solar orbit in a week.

The solarnauts on board were engaged on a scientific mission to collect particles of solar matter from the outer reaches of the sun. This would prove invaluable material for study back on Earth.

Three solarnauts remained aboard
while the nose-cone probe was
launched to collect particles from a
solar prominence and then retrieved.

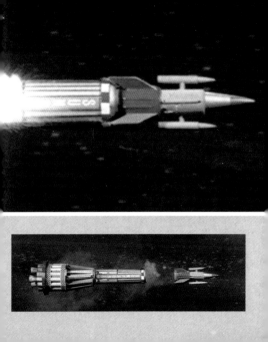

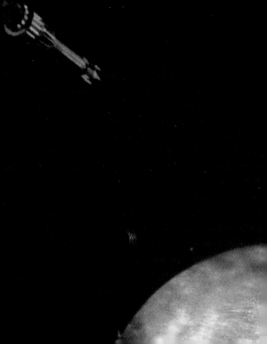

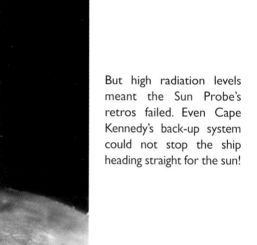

But high radiation levels meant the Sun Probe's retros failed. Even Cape Kennedy's back-up system could not stop the ship heading straight for the sun!

The spacecraft is housed in a deep silo concealed beneath the Round House, some distance from the Tracy Villa. Here, it rests on three immense columns which absorb the blast during take-off.

Once pilot Alan Tracy has taken his place at the cockpit controls, Thunderbird 3 is ready for blast off.

The rocket is launched on chemical rockets fed by helium-pressurized rocket propellant, and can quickly accelerate to escape velocity.

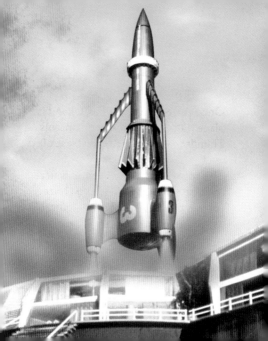

Once escape velocity is achieved – at the blistering speed of 25,200 m.p.h. – three particle accelerators powered by atomic generators provide a steady, continuous acceleration by means of an exhaust stream of atomic particles.

The ship's course is controlled
by a flywheel rotor assemblage,
although the rocket is also
equipped with pitch-and-yaw
correction jets.

The basic crew complement is
two, which usually means that
Scott will accompany Alan on
each space mission.

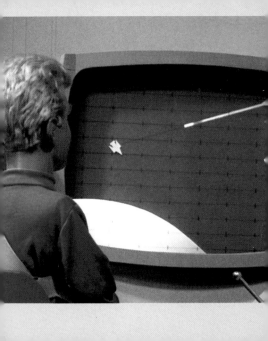

The craft houses the lounge, cockpit and rudimentary sleeping accommodation within a twin-walled hull which provides additional meteor protection, and the nose cone contains the craft's sensors, accelerometers and other flight instruments.

Thunderbird 3 has plenty of room for extra passengers and crew. Tin-Tin Kyrano's degrees in higher mathematics, advanced technical theory and engineering make her a very useful additional crewmember on Thunderbird 3 when a really dangerous situation arises.

THUNDERBIRD 3

CROSS-SECTIONS

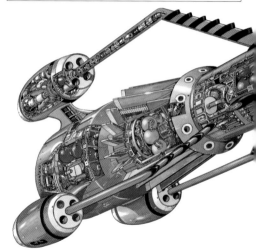

With Scott & Tin-Tin as his crew, Alan set Thunderbird 3 on a course for the sun. Their only chance to rescue the stranded solarnauts was to fire the Sun Probe's retros from space…

Thunderbird 3 was pushed to the limits of endurance, but the rocket's radio safety beam eventually fired the retros. The Sun Probe and its occupants were able to return home safely.

SPACE RESCUES

THE RICOCHET AFFAIR

Pirate satellite TV station KLA illustrates the problems of unlicensed broadcasting and the hazards of unregistered satellite usage. Because the station was unlicensed, its orbit was not registered with International Space Control.

Some months after KLA started operations, the ISC authorized the destruction of a Telstat IV Satellite Launcher, unaware that the station would be caught in the resulting explosion.

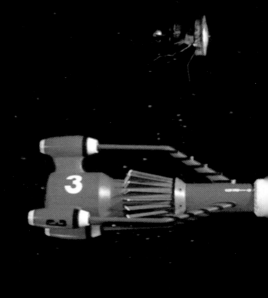

Knocked out of its orbit, KLA was unable to use its damaged breaking retros or parachutes. Luckily, following an on-air appeal for help, Thunderbird 3 was soon racing to the rescue.

THUNDERBIRD 3

After undertaking a daring space walk, Alan was able to rescue the DJ and his technical operator Loman before the satellite entered Earth's atmosphere.

ALAN TRACY

Named after 20th century astronaut Alan B. Shephard, Alan Tracy was born on 12 March 2044 and is now twenty-one years old.

Caring and deeply romantic, he has a love of motor-racing and was a champion racing-car driver prior to becoming the pilot of Thunderbird 3.

Educated at Colorado University, Alan is a great sportsman and practical joker. However, he is not without his quiet side and likes nothing better than to explore the rocks and potholes located in the more inaccessible points of Tracy Island.

The blond-haired, baby-faced astronaut is utterly dedicated to International Rescue, meeting his great responsibilities with a maturity that belies his years. Apart from piloting Thunderbird 3, Alan also assists his brother John by taking turns at manning the space station, Thunderbird 5.

THUNDERBIRD 3

The primary function of Thunderbird 3 is to act as a regular link to the Thunderbird 5 satellite in space for servicing and personnel transfer.

But the spacecraft doubles as a rescue vehicle on the rare occasions when it is required for operations in Earth orbit and outer space.

Alan relishes such opportunities, and likes to test himself and his craft to the limit.

There are times when Alan's father still just sees him as the student whose experiments with rockets went very wrong indeed, and accordingly treats him as a wayward schoolboy. Even so – a true man of action – Alan participates in most missions, often accompanying Virgil in Thunderbird 2.

THUNDERBIRD 3

With his extensive experience in motor racing and all things mechanical, he's expert at handling Thunderbird 2's Pod vehicles — such as the Booster Mortar.

While he detests violence, Alan is a keen marksman – which makes him an ideal choice to fire Thunderbird 2's tranquilizer guns when necessary!

He's even been known to fly TB1
– including a memorable rescue
operation in the Atlantic when
Scott was acting commander of
International Rescue.

When off-duty, Alan jealously guards his romantic relationship with Tin-Tin Kyrano — although he secretly harbours a passion for London agent Lady Penelope Creighton-Ward.

TECHNICAL DATA

LENGTH: .... 287 feet
NACELLE SPAN: .... 80 feet
MAIN BODY DIAMETER: ..... 23 feet
WEIGHT: .... 562 tons
LAUNCH THRUST: .... 4.5 million pounds
STANDARD ACCELERATION: 1 g
MAXIMUM SUSTAINED ACCELERATION: 6 g
EMERGENCY ACCELERATION: 10 g
RANGE: .... unlimited
POWER SOURCE: .... atomic fusion
                        reactor
ENGINES:

>   3 chemical rockets used for
>   launch, landing, emergency
>   boost and orbit change
>   3 ion-drive particle accelerators
>   used in deep space
>   Pitch and yaw rockets: 12 in
>   middle ring for course
>   corrections, 20 in nose and
>   24 at rear for attitude
>   adjustments

PILOT: .... Alan Tracy

Round House

When the main house is full, the Tracys' guests can be accommodated in this luxury alternative. What they will never guess, though, is that beneath them are the hangar and launch bay for Thunderbird 3, which rises vertically through the hollow centre of the house.

THUNDERBIRD 3

SECRET LOCATION · IR HEADQUARTERS · TRACY ISLAND

Thunderbird 5

Thunderbird 2

THUNDERBIRD 3

PUT IN PERSPECTIVE

Thunderbird 1

Thunderbird 4

Thunderbird 3